What you need to know about the National Tests

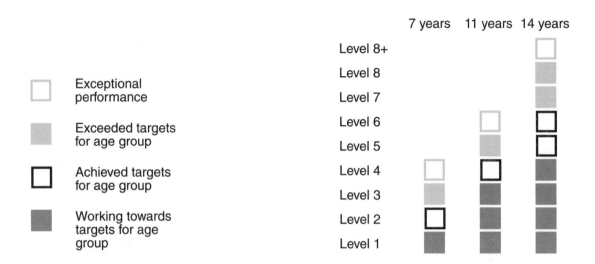

Exceptional performance

Exceeded targets for age group

Achieved targets for age group

Working towards targets for age group

How you should progress

This book concentrates on Levels 4–7. This means that you will find plenty of questions to practise, regardless of which tier you are entered for. The bar chart below shows you what percentage of students nationally reached each of the levels in the 1998 tests for Science.

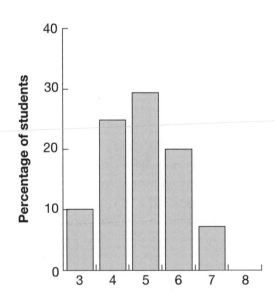

Levels achieved in Science, 1998

Preparing and practising for the Science Test

SCIENCE AT KEY STAGE 3

The questions in this book will test you on the Key Stage 3 curriculum for Science. For assessment purposes, the National Curriculum divides Science into four sections, called Attainment Targets (ATs). The first AT, Scientific Investigation, is assessed only by the teacher in the classroom, not in the written tests. The other three ATs are:

AT2: Life Processes and Living Things (which is largely Biology)
AT3: Materials and their Properties (which is largely Chemistry)
AT4: Physical Processes (which is largely Physics)

The National Curriculum describes levels of performance for each of the four Science ATs. These AT levels are taken together to give an overall level for Science. The test papers have questions covering each of ATs 2–4.

USING THIS BOOK TO HELP YOU PREPARE

This book contains four basic features:

Questions:	two test papers for Levels 4–7 and one extension paper for Levels 6–7
Answers:	showing acceptable responses and marks
Examiner's Tips:	giving advice on how to avoid common mistakes and improve your score
Level Charts:	showing you how to interpret your marks to arrive at a level for each test, as well as an overall level

SITTING THE TESTS AT HOME

Take Test A first. Mark the test to see how you have done, working through the answers and advice given. Then take Test B on a different day. You should carry out the tests in a place where you are comfortable. You will need a pencil, a rubber and a ruler. Make sure to read the instructions on page vi carefully before you begin.

Note the starting time in the box at the top of each test. Time yourself during the test, using a clock, a watch, or the help of a parent or friend. During the test, if you do not understand a word, you can ask a parent or other adult to explain what the word means, providing it is not a scientific word. For example, you could ask someone to explain what is meant by the word 'function' but not 'evaporation' or 'pressure'.

After 60 minutes, stop writing. If you have not finished, but wish to continue working on the test, draw a line to show how much has been completed within the test time. Then continue for as long as you wish.

Preparing and practising for the Science Test

MARKING THE QUESTIONS

When you have completed a test, turn to the Answers section at the back of the book. Work through the answers, using the advice in the Examiner's Tips to correct mistakes and explain problems. If you required extra time to complete a test, go through all the answers, but do not include the marks for the 'extra' questions in the total scores.

Using the recommended answers, award yourself the appropriate mark or marks for each question. In the margin of each test page, there are small boxes divided in half. The marks available for each question are at the bottom; write your score in the top half of the box.

Enter the total number of marks for each question on the Marking Grid on page 66. Then add them up to find the total for the test. Look at the Level Charts on page 65 to determine your level for each test, as well as an overall level.

If you have achieved at least Level 5 in Tests A and B you might want to try the Extension paper which is intended for assessing Levels 6 and 7. This test should take 45 minutes and again you can work out your level by using the grid on page 66.

You may wish to find out in which ATs you are strongest and which you are weakest. This may help you to plan your revision. Each marking grid shows which AT each question is testing. Count up the number of marks you have scored in each AT in each test.

FINALLY, AS THE TESTS DRAW NEAR

In the days before the tests, make sure you are as relaxed and confident as possible. You can help yourself by:

* ensuring you know what test papers you will be doing;

* working through practice questions, and learning which answers are right and why.

Above all, don't worry too much! Although the National Tests are important, your achievement throughout the school year is equally important. Do your best in these tests; that is all anyone can ask.

Instructions

Test A and Test B should each take 60 minutes; the Extension paper should take 45 minutes.

Try to answer all the questions.

Read the questions carefully. Sometimes you will use your knowledge to answer the questions. Other times the question will give you a situation you have not met before. When this is the case, you will be given all the information you need to answer the question.

If you think, after reading a question carefully, that you cannot answer it, leave the question and come back to it later.

The questions you have to answer are given in orange boxes. For example,

> **Explain what happens to the speed of the yacht when the sail is lowered.**

Write your answers fully on the test papers in this book. The ▭▷ shows where you should answer the question. The lines or space given should give you some indication of what is expected.

Look at the number of marks for each part of a question. This is shown in the box in the margin, for example,

2

If a question is worth one mark, often a single word or single point is needed. A question worth two marks would need two distinct points to be made. You are very unlikely to score two marks with a single word answer.

Look carefully at the words you write, particularly scientific words. Read your answers carefully to yourself and make sure you have clearly expressed what you mean.

GOOD LUCK!

Contents

What you need to know about the National Tests

KEY STAGE 3 NATIONAL TESTS: HOW THEY WORK

Students between the ages of 11 and 14 (Years 7–9) cover Key Stage 3 of the National Curriculum. In May of their final year of Key Stage 3 (Year 9), all students take written National Tests (commonly known as SATs) in English, Mathematics and Science. The tests are carried out in school, under the supervision of teachers, but are marked by examiners outside the school.

The tests help to show what you have learned in these key subjects. They also help parents and teachers to know whether students are reaching the standards set out in the National Curriculum. The results may be used by your teacher to help place you in the appropriate teaching group for some of your GCSE courses.

You will probably spend around seven hours in total sitting the tests during one week in May. Most students will do two test papers in each of English, Maths and Science.

The school sends the papers away to external examiners for marking. The school will then report the results of the tests to you and your parents by the end of July, along with the results of assessments made by teachers in the classroom, based on your work throughout Key Stage 3. You will also receive a summary of the results for all students at the school, and for students nationally. This will help you to compare your performance with that of other students of the same age. The report from your school will explain to you what the results show about your progress, strengths, particular achievements and targets for development. It may also explain how to follow up the results with your teachers.

UNDERSTANDING YOUR LEVEL OF ACHIEVEMENT

The National Curriculum divides standards for performance in each subject into a number of levels, from one to eight. On average, students are expected to advance one level for every two years they are at school. By Year 9 (the end of Key Stage 3), you should be at Level 5 or 6. The table on page iii shows how you are expected to progress through the levels at ages 7, 11 and 14 (the end of Key Stages 1, 2 and 3).

There are different National Test papers for different ability levels. This is to ensure that you can show positive achievement on the test, and not be discouraged by trying to answer questions which are too easy or too difficult. For Science, the tests are grouped into two ranges of levels, called 'tiers'. The two tiers cover Levels 3–6 and Levels 5–7. Your teachers will decide which tier you should be entered for. Each tier has two test papers. Each paper will be one hour long. Extension papers with high level questions (Level 8) are also available for exceptionally able students.

Start [   ]   Finish [   ]

1 Two balloons are rubbed with a duster and each balloon gains a negative charge. The balloons are hung from the ceiling using pieces of string.

a

> Do the balloons attract or repel each other?

....
....

b

> Does the duster gain a positive or a negative charge?

....

c

> Which diagram shows the position of the balloons?

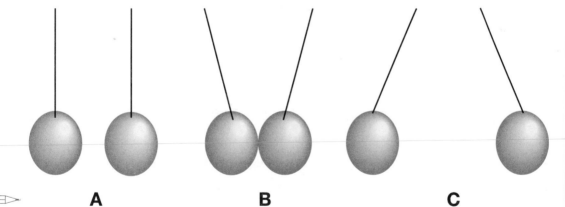

   A   **B**   **C**

d The duster is held near one of the balloons.

> Do the balloon and the duster attract or repel each other?
> Give the reason for your answer.

....
....

Letts

Test A

2 The diagram shows a foxglove flower with a bumble bee inside it.

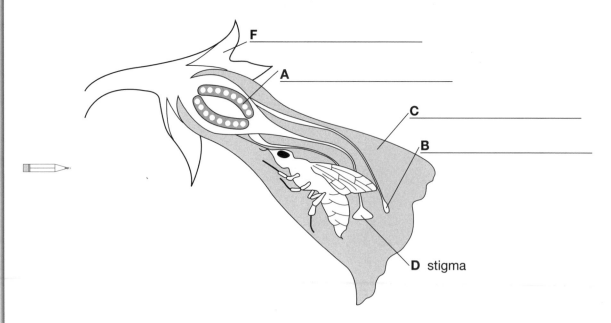

F _____

A _____

C _____

B _____

D stigma

a

> Add labels to the diagram to show the names of the parts. Choose the best words from this list.

anther   leaf   ovary   petal   pollen   sepal   stamen

b The table shows the jobs done by different parts of the flower.

> Choose a letter from the diagram above to finish the table. One has been done for you.

Job of the part of the flower	Letter from diagram
Catches the pollen by giving a flat sticky surface.	D
Attracts the bumble bee to the flower.	
Makes and stores pollen	
Protects the flower bud	
Makes and produces ovules	

c

> **What is the bumble bee taking from the flower and what is this used for?**

✏️ ....

....

2

Q2c

d

> **Why does the shape of the flower make the process work well?**

✏️ ....

....

2

Q2d

e

> **Explain the difference between the processes of *pollination* and *fertilisation*.**

✏️ ....

....

2

Q2e

3   Three circuits are shown in the diagram.

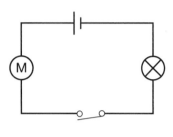 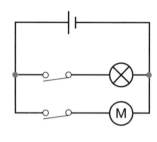 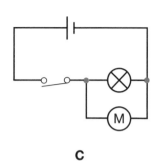

A   B   C

a
> **Complete the following sentences:**

(i)   The lamp and the motor are connected in series in circuit.................

(ii) The lamp and the motor must have the same current in circuit ....

(iii) The lamp and the motor are both worked by the same switch in

circuits .... and ....

b
> **What instrument would you use to measure the current in circuit A?**

....

c   The current that passes into the lamp in circuit B is 0.3 A.

> **How much current does the lamp use up?**

....

d
> **Write down one way of increasing the current that passes in the lamp in circuit B.**

....

4   The table gives some information about changes that occur when copper and three copper compounds are heated in air. In each case 1.0 g of the substance is heated

Substance	Appearance before heating	Appearance after heating	Mass of solid residue
Copper	brown colour	black coating	1.1 g
Copper(II) carbonate	pale green powder	black powder	0.7 g
Copper(II) oxide	black powder	black powder	1.0 g
Copper(II) sulphate crystals	blue crystals	white powder	0.7 g

a

Which of these substances does not change on heating?

   ....

1

Q4a

b

Explain why copper increases in mass when heated in air but copper(II) carbonate decreases.

....

....

....

....

4

Q4b

c   Heating copper(II) sulphate crystals is a temporary change.

Describe what you would see if cold water is dropped onto the white powder formed when copper(II) sulphate crystals are heated.

....

....

2

Q4c

Test A

5   The diagram shows the human digestive system.

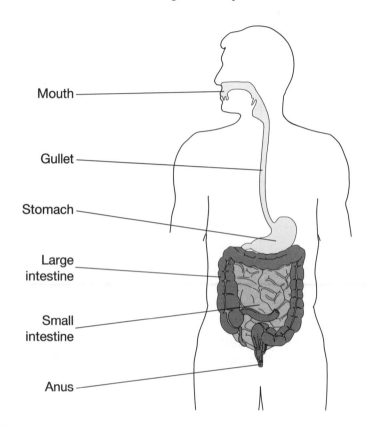

Mouth

Gullet

Stomach

Large intestine

Small intestine

Anus

a

Match each named organ with its job. Draw a line from each organ to the job it does. One has been done for you.

Organ	Job of the organ
Anus	absorbs dissolved food into the blood
Gullet	chews the food into small pieces
Large intestine	dissolves the food
Mouth	passes the food to the stomach
Small intestine	passes solid waste out of the body
Stomach	absorbs water from the waste

MARKS

b The process of digestion starts in the mouth.

> **What is present in saliva to start the process of digestion?**

....

c Sugar molecules are absorbed into the bloodstream but starch molecules are not.

> **What is the important difference between sugar and starch molecules that explains this?**

....

6 The pink colouring from rose petals can be used as an indicator for acids and alkalis. The colouring is not soluble in water but soluble in ethanol.

a

> **Describe how a solution of this pink colouring could be made from rose petals.**

....

....

....

....

b   The table gives the colour of pink rose petal colouring, phenolphthalein and methyl orange indicators in acidic, neutral and alkaline solutions.

Indicator	Colour in acidic solution	Colour in neutral solution	Colour in alkaline solution
pink rose petal solution	pink	pink	green
phenolphthalein	colourless	colourless	pink
methyl orange	red	orange	orange

(i)

What is the pH value of a neutral solution?

1

Q6b(i)

(ii)

What colour would pink rose petal solution turn in sodium hydroxide solution?

1

Q6b(ii)

(iii)

How can phenolphthalein and methyl orange indicators be used to show that a solution is neutral?

2

Q6b(iii)

7 The table shows the times taken by some children to swim 80 m in a race.

Swimmer	Time taken
Adam	27 s
Natalie	20 s
Kinglun	25 s
Claire	32 s
Faiza	29 s

a

> Who was the fastest swimmer?

....

Q7a

b

> Who came last?

....

Q7b

c

> Work out Natalie's speed in m/s.

speed = ... m/s.

Q7c

Letts

Test A

8   The diagrams show a plant cell and an animal cell.

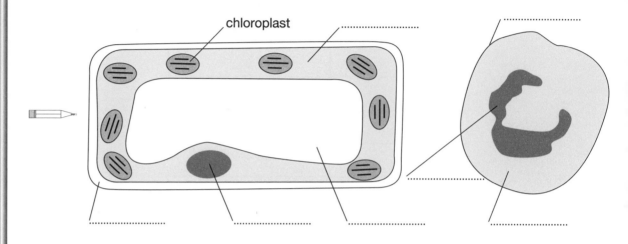

chloroplast

a   Use words from this list to label the diagrams. You may use each
    word once, more than once or not at all.

cell membrane   cell wall   cytoplasm   nucleus   vacuole

b   What is the job of the chloroplasts?

....

c   Where in each cell is the genetic information stored?

....

Respiration takes place in all cells.

Use words from this list to answer the questions.

carbon dioxide   energy   glucose   oxygen   water

d

> **Which two substances are used up during respiration?**

.... and ....

2

Q8d

e

> **Which two substances are produced during respiration?**

.... and ....

2

Q8e

f

> **What is released during respiration?**

....

1

Q8f

9   The diagram shows a drawing pin.

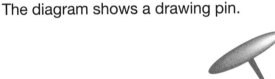

a

> **What two features of the drawing pin enable it to exert a large pressure?**

....

....

2

Q9a

b   A tank weighs 60 000 N and the area of the caterpillar tracks touching the ground is 20 m².

> **Work out the pressure on the ground in N/m².**

pressure = ... N/m²

2

Q9b

Test A

10 The table gives some information about five elements.

Element	Melting point in °C	Boiling point in °C	Dull or shiny	Electrical conductivity
Phosphorus	44	280	dull	nil
Iron	1535	3000	shiny	good
Mercury	−39	357	shiny	good
Sulphur	113	444	dull	nil
Sodium	98	890	shiny	good

a

Which element is liquid at room temperature (20 °C)?

....

1

Q10a

b

Which element is liquid over the smallest range of temperature?

....

1

Q10b

c The bar chart shows the boiling points of some of the elements.

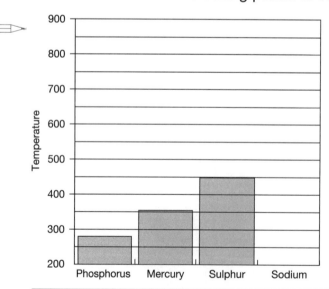

Finish the bar chart by adding the boiling point of sodium.

1

Q10c

d

> Which of these elements are metals and which are non-metals?

Metals ....

Non-metals ....

e

> How could you separate iron from other metals?

....

....

f Sodium and sulphur burn in oxygen to form oxides.

> How do these two oxides differ when Universal indicator solution is added?

....

....

MARKS

11 The diagram shows an audience watching a play in a theatre.

a

> **Underline the objects shown in the diagram that give out light.**

✎➤ **actors   audience   stage lights**

1
Q11a

b

> **Explain how a person in the audience sees the actors.**

✎➤ ....

....

2
Q11b

c Stage lights are often fitted with colour filters.

> **Underline the colours that can pass through a cyan (turquoise) filter.**

✎➤ **blue   cyan   green   magenta   red   yellow**

2
Q11c

d An actress wears a yellow costume. The stage is lit with red light.

> **What colour does her costume appear to be?**

✎➤ ....

1
Q11d

Letts

MARKS

12   The diagrams show the position of the Sun in the sky at midday in spring and in winter.

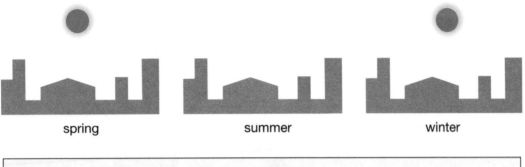

spring   summer   winter

a   Draw the position of the Sun in summer.

1

Q12a

b   Explain why the Sun is in a different position in summer and in winter.

....

....

2

Q12b

13a   Underline the energy sources in the list that are non-renewable.

biomass   coal   oil   wind

2

Q13a

b   A new power-station is built that will grow its own fuel; wood from fast-growing willow trees.

(i)   Explain whether wood is a renewable or non-renewable energy source.

....

1

Q13b(i)

(ii)   Give one advantage of using wood as a fuel to generate electricity.

....

1

Q13b(ii)

Letts

14 Five groups of students carried out an experiment. They burnt different masses of magnesium ribbon in air. Each group found the mass of magnesium oxide produced.

The apparatus they used is shown in the diagram below.

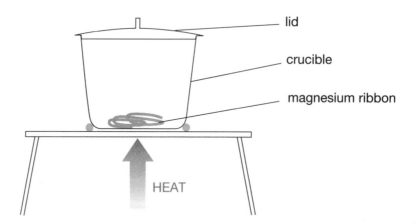

a

> **Why is it necessary to lift the lid from time to time during the experiment but not to let any smoke out?**

....

....

2

Q14a

The results of their experiments are shown in the graph opposite.

b

> **What mass of magnesium did Group B use?**

1

Q14b

....

c

> **What mass of oxygen combined with the magnesium in Group B's experiment?**

1

Q14c

....

Letts

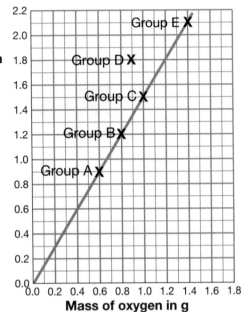

Mass of
magnesium
in g

Mass of oxygen in g

d(i)

Why do you think there was unreacted magnesium left in the crucible after Group D's experiment?

....

1

Q14d(i)

(ii)

Describe a test you would use to show this.

Test ....

Result ....

2

Q14d(ii)

e The textbook states that magnesium also reacts with nitrogen.

What is the name of the compound formed between magnesium and nitrogen?

....

1

Q14e

17

Test B

Start		Finish	

1a The diagram shows the magnetic field pattern of a bar magnet.

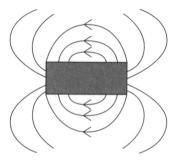

Label the poles on the magnet.

1
Q1a

b The diagram shows two magnets that are repelling each other.

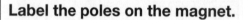

S	N			

(i) | **Label the poles on the right-hand magnet.** |
|---|

1
Q1b(i)

(ii) | **Draw an arrow on the diagram that shows the force on the right-hand magnet.** |
|---|

1
Q1b(ii)

2 The diagrams opposite show four methods which can be used to separate mixtures of substances.

a

Match up the name of the method with the correct diagram by writing the letters P, Q, R and S in the boxes.

Name of the method	Letter
Chromatography	
Filtration	
Distillation	
Fractional distillation	

3
Q2a

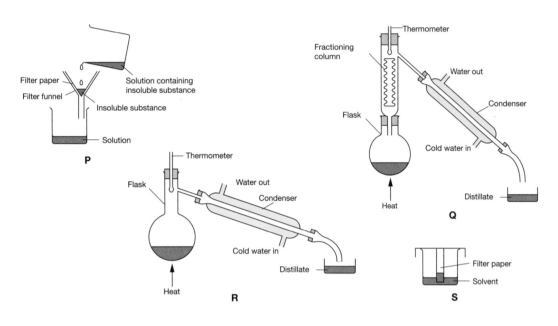

b Here is a list of mixtures which could be separated.

A A solution of wax dissolved in hexane.

B A mixture of a solid residue and water.

C A mixture of coloured dyes in solution.

D A mixture of two miscible liquids hexane and heptane.

(i)

Which mixture could be separated by filtration?

1

Q2b(i)

(ii)

Which mixture could be separated by chromatography?

1

Q2b(ii)

(iii)

Which mixture could be separated by fractional distillation?

1

Q2b(iii)

MARKS

3 Sparrowhawks eat great tits. Aphids eat leaves. Great tits eat ladybirds. Ladybirds eat aphids.

a

> **Complete the food chain.**

2

Q3a

✏️➤ leaves ⟶

b

> **Which living thing is the producer in the food chain?**

1

Q3b

✏️➤ ....

c

> **Explain why the great tit is both a *predator* and *prey*.**

1

Q3c(i)

✏️➤ **(i)** predator ....

1

Q3c(ii)

✏️➤ **(ii)** prey ....

d In a hot summer the aphid population increases very quickly.

> **Explain how this affects the population of ladybirds.**

✏️➤ ....

2

Q3d

....

Here is a food web.

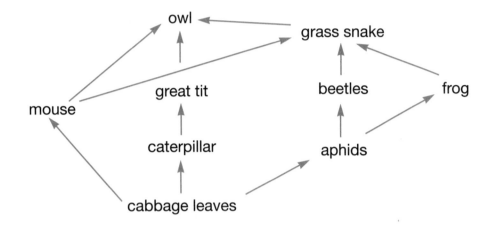

e

> **Name one herbivore shown in the food web.**

✏ ....

1

Q3e

f During one summer there is a shortage of beetles.

> **Explain why this has little effect on the number of grass snakes.**

✏ ....

1

Q3f

Letts

4   Experiments were carried out with four metals, **W**, **X**, **Y** and **Z**. The diagrams show the results obtained when pieces of the four metals were added to dilute hydrochloric acid. Three of the test tubes were then heated and the results are also shown.

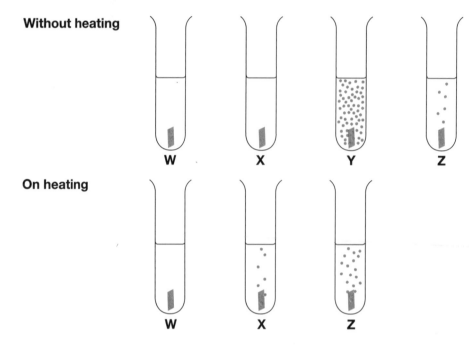

Without heating

W   X   Y   Z

On heating

W   X   Z

a

> **Use the results of these reactions to put these four metals in order of decreasing reactivity.**

Most reactive   Least reactive

☐   ☐   ☐   ☐

3
Q4a

b(i)

> **Write down the name of the gas formed when Y reacts with dilute hydrochloric acid.**

....

1
Q4b(i)

(ii)

> **How would you test for this gas?**

Test ....

Result ....

2
Q4b(ii)

5   The diagram shows an electromagnet made by passing a current in a coil of wire.

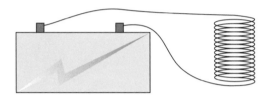

a

> **What could you use to investigate the magnetic field around the coil of wire?**

In the next diagram a core has been placed inside the coil.

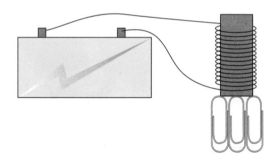

b

> **Which material would make the strongest electromagnet?**
> **Underline your choice.**

brass   iron   paper   wood

c

> **Explain why this material makes the electromagnet stronger.**

Test B

6   The diagram shows some of the organs in a human body.

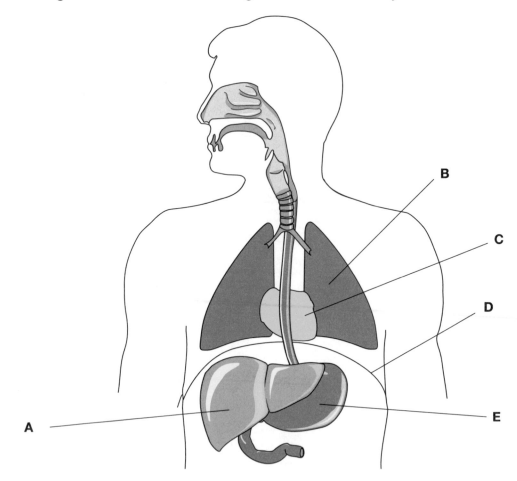

Draw lines to match the letter of each organ to the job it does.

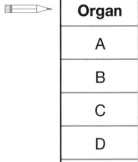

Organ		Job of the organ
A		pumps blood around the body
B		processes nitrogen waste (urea)
C		expands and contracts the lungs
D		digests food
E		exchanges gases between air and blood

5

Q6

Test B

SAINT BENEDICT SCHOOL
DUFFIELD ROAD
DERBY DE22 1JD

TEST B
LEVELS 4-7

MARKS

7 The diagram shows three circuits.

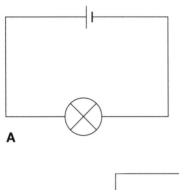

A

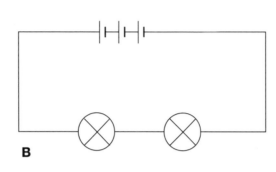

B

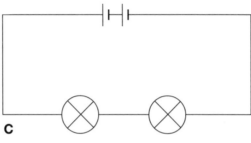

C

a

> **What could you use to measure the current in circuit A? Draw the symbol on the diagram.**

....

2
Q7a

b

> **In which circuit do the cells run down the quickest?**

....

1
Q7b

c

> **Explain why the cells run down quickest in this circuit.**

....

....

2
Q7c

MARKS

Q8a

1

Q8b

1

Q8c(i)

1

Q8c(ii)

1

Q8c(iii)

1

8 Iron and sulphur are elements. When they are mixed together and the mixture is heated in a test tube, a reaction takes place. A glow spreads throughout the mixture even if the test tube is taken out of the flame.

a

> **What does the glow spreading through the mixture show about the reaction?**

....

b

> **Write down the name of the compound formed when iron and sulphur combine.**

....

c In the diagram below

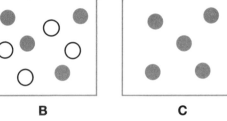

● stands for a zinc atom   ○ stands for a sulphur atom

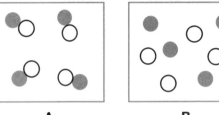 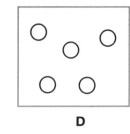

A   B   C   D

(i)

> **Which diagram represents pure sulphur?**

☐

(ii)

> **Which diagram represents a mixture of zinc and sulphur?**

☐

(iii)

> **Which diagram represents a compound of zinc and sulphur?**

☐

9 The diagram shows a boat floating on water. The arrow represents one of the forces that acts on the boat.

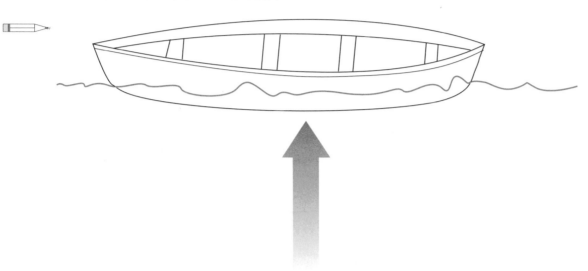

a

> **Choose words from the list to complete the sentence that describes the force.**

boat   downward   Earth   upward   water

The arrow shows the .... push of the

.... on the ....

3
Q9a

b

> **Draw an arrow on the diagram to show another force that acts on the boat when it is floating.**

1
Q9b

Two people climb into the boat.

c

> **How does this affect the size of the downward force?**

....

1
Q9c

d

> **How does this affect the size of the upward force?**

....

1
Q9d

10 The diagram shows part of an arm.

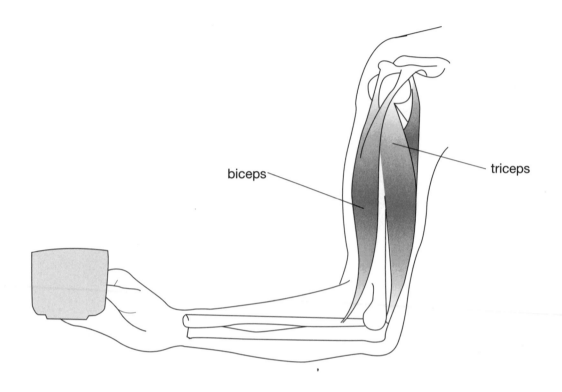

biceps

triceps

a What type of joint is the shoulder?

  ....

1

Q10a

b Why is this type of joint found at the shoulder?

  ....

1

Q10b

c Use the words *contract* and *relax* to describe what happens to the biceps and triceps when the cup is lifted.

  ....

....

2

Q10c

11 A balanced diet contains fat, fibre, carbohydrate, minerals, vitamins and water.

a

> **Which food chemical gives a ready supply of energy?**

....

....

Q11a

b

> **Which important food chemical is missing from the list?**

....

....

Q11b

c The diagrams show some everyday foods.

bread   cheese   orange   cabbage

(i)

> **Which food is the best source of fat?**

....

Q11c(i)

(ii)

> **Which food is the best source of calcium?**

....

Q11c(ii)

(iii)

> **Why is it important to include calcium in a healthy diet?**

....

Q11c(iii)

Test B

Test B

12 Ice, liquid water and steam all contain the same water particles.

a

> **Describe the arrangement and movement of particles in liquid water.**

Arrangement ....

....

Movement ....

....

4

Q12a

b When a saucer filled with liquid water is left on a window sill, the water evaporates.

(i)

> **Explain in terms of particles what is happening when liquid water evaporates.**

....

....

2

Q12b(i)

(ii)

> **Why does evaporation occur faster when there is a draught in the room?**

....

....

1

Q12b(ii)

(iii)

> **In certain hot countries, a thin layer of oil is put onto the surface of the water in reservoirs. Why?**

....

....

1

Q12b(iii)

13a The diagram shows a xylem cell taken from the stem of a plant.

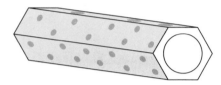

(i)

> **What substance is transported in the xylem cell?**

....

1

Q13a(i)

(ii)

> **Which part of the plant does this substance come from?**

....

1

Q13a(ii)

b In daylight, green plants make food in a process called photosynthesis.

This equation describes the process of photosynthesis.

carbon dioxide + water $\longrightarrow$ sugar + oxygen

(i)

> **What waste product is produced during photosynthesis?**

....

1

Q13b(i)

(ii)

> **How does the plant get rid of this waste product?**

....

....

2

Q13b(ii)

(iii)

> **What is the energy source for photosynthesis?**

....

1

Q13b(iii)

c An ivy plant has leaves that are green and yellow.

Which part of the leaf produces the most sugar?

....

d The graph shows how sugar produced by a tomato plant growing in a greenhouse changes over a period of several days.

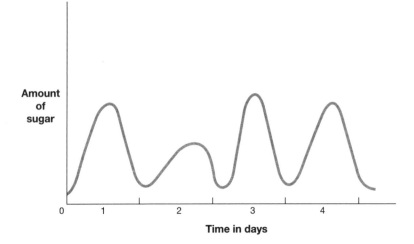

Amount of sugar

Time in days

(i)

Explain why the rate of sugar production varies.

....

(ii)

How could the tomato grower change the air in the greenhouse to increase the rate of sugar production?

....

14 The order of reactivity of four metals is:

Magnesium
Zinc
Copper
Silver

Tests were carried out by putting these four metals into solutions of the four different metal nitrates.

The results were recorded in a table.

	Copper nitrate	Magnesium nitrate	Silver nitrate	Zinc nitrate
Copper	✗	✗	✓	✗
Magnesium		✗		
Silver			✗	
Zinc				✗

a

Finish the table by putting a tick (✓) if a reaction takes place or a cross(✗) if a reaction does not.

3

Q14a

b

What would you *see* when copper reacts with silver nitrate solution?

....

....

2

Q14b

c

Finish the word equation for the reaction of copper with silver nitrate solution.

copper + silver nitrate ⟶ .... + ...

2

Q14c

15   The diagram shows the driving force and the resistive force acting on a yacht.

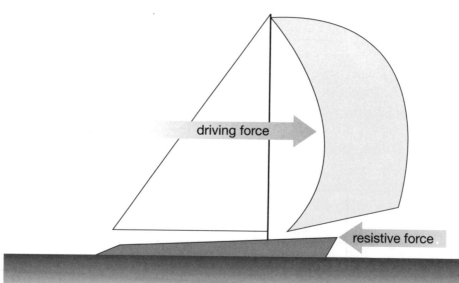

a

What causes the driving force?

....

b

Explain why the yacht is speeding up.

....

c

Explain what happens to the speed of the yacht when the sail is lowered.

....

....

16a

> Which diagram shows reflection of light at a mirror correctly?

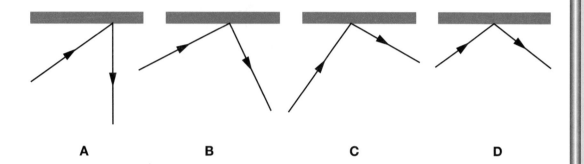

| A | B | C | D |

 ....

b

> Explain how the reflection of light by a page of this book is different to the reflection of light at a mirror.

....

A candle is placed in front of a mirror.

candle

A   E

B   D

          C

c

> Which letter shows the position of the image of the candle?

....

d

> Write down *two* ways in which the candle and its image are similar.

1 ....

2 ....

17 The diagram shows a loudspeaker.

a

How does the loudspeaker produce a sound wave?

1

Q17a

....

b

How does the movement change to produce a sound wave with a bigger amplitude?

1

Q17b

....

c

How does the sound change when the amplitude of the sound wave is increased?

1

Q17c

....

MARKS

18 The diagram shows a satellite in orbit around the Earth.

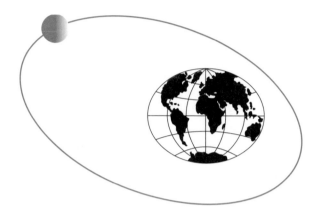

a

| Use an arrow to show the force that acts on the satellite. |

1
Q18a

b

| Write down *two* uses of artificial satellites. |

....

....

....

2
Q18b

Letts

Extension paper

Start		Finish	

1 The diagram shows a human fetus in the womb.

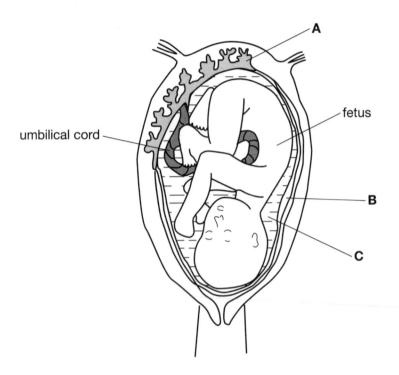

umbilical cord

fetus

A

B

C

a

Complete the table below by using words from the list that match the letters on the diagram.

amniotic fluid   amniotic sac   placenta   uterus

Letter	Label
A	
B	
C	

3
Q1a

b

What is the job of the umbilical cord?

....

....

....

2
Q1b

Extension paper

SAINT BENEDICT SCHOOL
DUFFIELD ROAD
DERBY DE22 1JD

EXTENSION PAPER
LEVELS 6–7

MARKS

2   John and Rebecca carry out an experiment. They both use leaves from the same plant. The apparatus was left in bright light for a few hours.

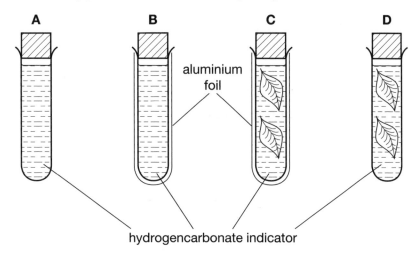

A   B   C   D

aluminium foil

hydrogencarbonate indicator

The table shows their results.

Tube	Colour of hydrogencarbonate indicator	
	At the start	After a few hours
A	red	red
B	red	red
C	red	yellow
D	red	purple

a

What is the job of tubes A and B?

1

Q2a

b

Explain the changes taking place in tubes C and D.

Tube **C** ....

....

Tube **D** ....

....

4

Q2b

Extension paper

3   This question is about how smoking cigarettes during pregnancy can affect the birthweight of babies.

The table shows the average number of cigarettes smoked each day by pregnant women and the average birthweights of their babies.

Average number of cigarettes smoked each day by pregnant women	Average birthweight of their babies in g
0	3000
10	2990
20	2965
30	2910
40	2800

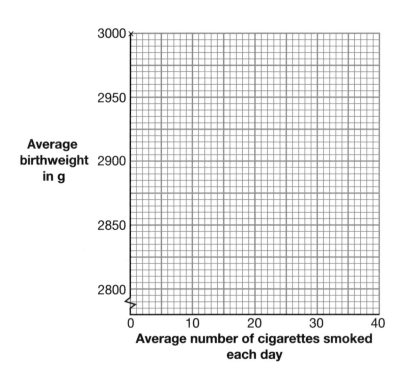

a

Plot these points on the grid. The first one has been done for you.

b

Finish the graph by drawing the best line.

1

Q3b

c

From your graph find the number of cigarettes which produces an average birthweight of 2900 g.

1

Q3c

....

d Smoking during pregnancy can harm the unborn baby.

Write down two other habits a pregnant woman might have that could harm her unborn baby.

1 ....

2 ....

2

Q3d

4 A lump of calcium carbonate, $CaCO_3$, is added to dilute hydrochloric acid, HCl. Bubbles of carbon dioxide gas, CO_2, are formed. Calcium chloride, $CaCl_2$, and water are also formed.

a

Write a word and balanced symbol equation for the reaction

Word equation ....

....

Symbol equation ....

....

3

Q4a

b

How would you test for carbon dioxide?

Test ....

Result ....

2

Q4b

41

Extension paper

c   The apparatus in the diagram is set up and carbon dioxide is bubbled through the water for several hours.

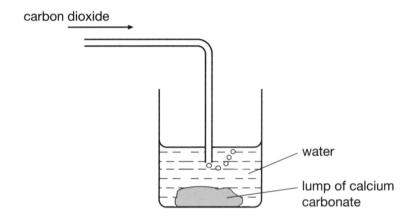

carbon dioxide

water

lump of calcium carbonate

> **Explain why the lump of calcium carbonate weighs less at the end of the experiment.**

....

....

....

3

Q4c

5a   The diagram opposite shows a rock exposed to air and water. At night the temperature drops below 0 °C. During the day the temperature rises to 20 °C.

(i)   > **Explain how this rock is broken up.**

....

....

....

....

3

Q5a(i)

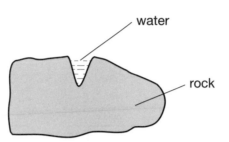

water

rock

(ii)

What name is given to this process?

1

Q5a(ii)

b Rocks are broken down in a desert without the help of water.

Explain *two* ways rocks can be broken down without water in the desert.

....

....

....

....

....

4

Q5b

**Extension
paper**

6a Complete the diagrams to show how white light passes through a
rectangular block of glass.

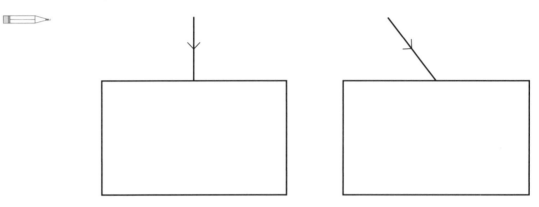

b As the light enters and leaves the glass its speed changes.

What name is given to this effect?

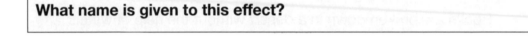

c White light can be dispersed as it passes through a triangular prism.

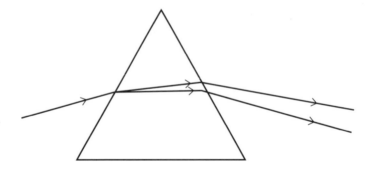

(i) **What happens to white light when it is dispersed?**

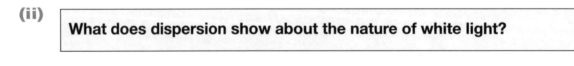

(ii) **What does dispersion show about the nature of white light?**

7 On a clear night, stars, planets and the Moon can be seen in the sky.

a Stars are seen by the light that they give out.

> **Describe how the Moon is seen.**

....

....

2

Q7a

b An astronomer takes a photograph of the sky at night.
Three hours later, she takes another photograph of the same part of the sky.
These are the photographs.

(i)

> **Which star appears in the same position?**

....

1

Q7b(i)

(ii)

> **Explain why the other stars appear to have moved.**

....

1

Q7b(ii)

(iii)

> **After taking the second photograph, how long would she have to wait to be able to see the stars in the same position as they were in the first photograph?**

....

1

Q7b(iii)

8 The graph shows how the distance that a cyclist travels changes with time.

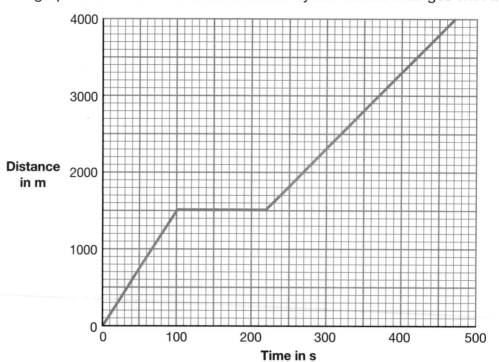

a

> **How far did the cyclist travel in the first 100 s?**

1

Q8a

....

b

> **For how long was the cyclist not moving?**

1

Q8b

....

c

> **Work out the cyclist's speed on the last section shown on the graph.**

3

Q8c

speed = ... m/s.

Answers

HOW TO MARK THE QUESTIONS

When marking your tests remember the answers given are sample answers and you must look at your answers and judge whether they deserve credit. Award the mark if the answer deserves credit.

You should pay special attention to spelling. There is no automatic penalty for a word that is misspelt. Look at the word as written and read it aloud. If it sounds correct and has the correct number of syllables, the mark can be awarded. For example, 'desolve' and 'weit' are acceptable for 'dissolve' and 'weight'. However, 'photosis' would not be accepted for 'photosynthesis'.

There is an emphasis on the correct spelling of scientific words. Look through this book and make a list of scientific words. Looking at this list and making sure you know the meaning of the words is good preparation in the few days before the tests.

When you go through the answers, try to work out where you have gone wrong. Make a note of the key points, so that you will remember them next time.

Enter your marks for each test on the Marking Grid on page 66, and then work out your level of achievement on these tests on page 65.

TEST A — Pages 1–17

1a Repel — *1 mark*

Examiner's tip

You should remember that things with the same type of charge repel each other, and those with opposite type of charge attract each other.

b Positive — *1 mark*

Examiner's tip

The balloon becomes charged by negatively charged electrons being transferred from the duster to the balloon. This results in the duster having a deficit of electrons, giving it an overall positive charge.

c C — *1 mark*
d They attract each other. — *1 mark*
They have opposite charges. — *1 mark*

TOTAL 5 MARKS

2a A – ovary — *1 mark*
B – anther — *1 mark*
C – petal — *1 mark*
F – sepal — *1 mark*
b C, B, F, A — *One mark each: 4 marks*
c The bumble bee takes nectar out of the flower — *1 mark*
which it uses for energy (or to make honey). — *1 mark*

d   The flower is tube shaped so the bumble bee does not easily leave the flower.   *1 mark*
        The bumble bee has to brush past the anthers to get the nectar.   *1 mark*
e   Pollination is the transfer of pollen from the stamen (or anther) to the stigma.   *1 mark*
        Fertilisation is the fusion of the male and female sex cells.   *1 mark*

TOTAL 14 MARKS

3a (i)   **A**   *1 mark*

  (ii)   **A**   *1 mark*
(iii)   **A** and **C** (either order)   *1 mark*
b   Ammeter   *1 mark*
c   None   *1 mark*

d   Increase the voltage.   *1 mark*

TOTAL 6 MARKS

4a Copper(II) oxide *1 mark*
b Copper reacts with oxygen in the air. *1 mark*
Black coating is copper(II) oxide. *1 mark*
Copper(II) carbonate decomposes (splits up). *1 mark*
Produces carbon dioxide which is lost. *1 mark*
c Any two from:
turns blue, steam produced, heat evolved *2 marks*

Examiner's tip

This question is about permanent and temporary changes which occur when substances are heated. A temporary change is one which can be reversed easily. For example, if ice is heated it turns to liquid water; if water is cooled, ice is reformed.

A permanent change is one which cannot be reversed, either by cooling or by mixing the products. For example, burning a piece of wood is a permanent change.

TOTAL 7 MARKS

5a

Organ	Job of the organ
Anus	absorbs dissolved food into the blood
Gullet	chews the food into small pieces
Large intestine	dissolves the food
Mouth	passes the food to the stomach
Small intestine	passes solid waste out of the body
Stomach	absorbs water from the waste

One mark for each correct link: 5 marks

Examiner's tip

It is important that you know the important steps in the digestion process. Students often get the jobs of the two intestines wrong. The food, in the form of a liquid, passes from the stomach into the small intestine. Here soluble substances pass into the blood. It then passes into the large intestine which absorbs water, leaving solid waste which passes out of the anus.

b Enzymes *1 mark*

Examiner's tip

You would not be penalised if you gave a correct name for a suitable enzyme.

c Sugar molecules are much smaller than starch molecules. *1 mark*

TOTAL 7 MARKS

6a	Cut up or crush up rose petals.	*1 mark*
	Add ethanol to petals.	*1 mark*
	Heat (using a water bath)	*1 mark*
	Filter off (or decant off) remains of petals.	*1 mark*
b (i)	pH 7	*1 mark*
(ii)	Green	*1 mark*
(iii)	In separate tests, phenolphthalein is colourless	*1 mark*
	and methyl orange is orange.	*1 mark*

Examiner's tip

In part **a** the answer could include some indication of hazards of heating ethanol with a naked flame.

In **d** the marks can only be awarded if it is appreciated that both colours are obtained. It is this combination which tells us the solution is neutral. Colourless and red would indicate an acid and pink and orange an alkali.

TOTAL 8 MARKS

7a	Natalie	*1 mark*

Examiner's tip

Natalie was the fastest because she completed the race in the shortest time.

b	Claire	*1 mark*

Examiner's tip

Claire took the longest time to complete the same distance as the other swimmers.

c	speed = distance ÷ time	*1 mark*
	= 80 m ÷ 20 s = 4 (m/s)	*1 mark*

Examiner's tip

When doing calculations you should always write out the formula first. This way, you get a mark for knowing the formula even if you make a mistake when working out the answer.

TOTAL 4 MARKS

8a	Seven correct labels.	*4 marks*

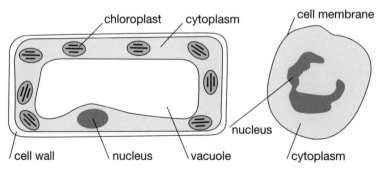

Count up number of correct labels, divide by two and round up to whole number.

b	They absorb the light energy needed for photosynthesis to take place.	*1 mark*
c	In the nucleus.	*1 mark*
d	glucose; oxygen	*2 marks*
e	carbon dioxide; water	*2 marks*
f	energy	*1 mark*

Examiner's tip

It is important to be able to distinguish plant and animal cells. Plant cells have a cell wall which give the cell shape and some rigidity.

TOTAL 11 MARKS

9a	The flat head	*1 mark*
	and the sharp point.	*1 mark*
b	pressure = force ÷ area	*1 mark*
	= 60 000 N ÷ 20 m² = 3000 (N/m²)	*1 mark*

Examiner's tip

This is another example where you should write down the formula that you are using before doing the calculation.

TOTAL 4 MARKS

10a	Mercury	*1 mark*
b	Phosphorus	*1 mark*

c

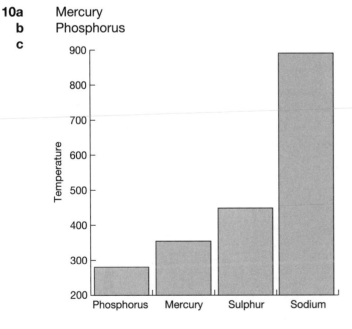

1 mark

d	Metals – iron, mercury and sodium	
	Non-metals – phosphorus, sulphur	*2 marks*
	One mark for a correct list of metals and one for a correct list of non-metals.	

51

Examiner's tip

You do not need to remember whether the elements are metals or non-metals. The properties in the table will help you decide. One problem caused by the marking scheme is that one error,e.g. writing that mercury is a non-metal will cost both marks.

e	Use a magnet	*1 mark*
	Iron will be attracted to the magnet but the others will not.	*1 mark*

Examiner's tip

Many students lose the second mark here. They refer to the magnet but do not explain how it is used to separate the iron.

f	Sodium oxide turns Universal indicator purple (strongly alkaline).	*1 mark*
	Sulphur dioxide turns Universal indicator red (strongly acidic).	*1 mark*

Examiner's tip

Non-metals burn to form acidic oxides. Metals burn to form neutral or alkaline oxides. A reactive metal, such as sodium, forms an alkaline oxide.

TOTAL 9 MARKS

11a	stage lights	*1 mark*
b	Light from the stage lights is reflected by the actor.	*1 mark*
	This reflected light enters the eyes of the audience.	*1 mark*

Examiner's tip

Mirrors and other shiny surfaces only reflect light in one direction. Other everyday objects scatter the light, this means that they reflect it in all directions. Objects that are not light sources are seen by the light that they scatter.

c	blue, cyan and green	*2 marks*

Examiner's tip

Award one mark for getting two colours correct.

d	red	*1 mark*

Examiner's tip

The yellow costume reflects red, green and yellow light. As yellow and green are not present in red light, it can only reflect the red.

TOTAL 6 MARKS

12a   The Sun should be drawn higher in the sky than in spring or winter.   *1 mark*

b   In summer the northern hemisphere is tilted towards the Sun.   *1 mark*

    In winter the northern hemisphere is tilted away from the Sun   *1 mark*

Examiner's tip

Award one mark for an answer such as 'it is because the Earth is tilted on its axis'.

TOTAL 3 MARKS

13a   coal and oil   *One mark each: 2 marks*

b (i)   Wood is renewable because more can be grown.   *1 mark*

Examiner's tip

Do not award a mark for the answer that wood is renewable. The reason why wood is renewable is also needed, since the question asks you to 'explain'.

(ii)   Less fossil fuels such as coal need to be burned.   *1 mark*

Examiner's tip

Award a mark if you answered along the lines that coal or other fossil fuels will last longer.

TOTAL 4 MARKS

14a   The lid has to be lifted to allow air (oxygen) to enter the crucible.   *1 mark*

    If smoke is lost the mass of the magnesium oxide is reduced.   *1 mark*

b   1.2 g   *1 mark*

c   0.8 g   *1 mark*

Examiner's tip

You get the answers to parts **b** and **c** from the graph.

d (i)   Their point is not on the line and there is less oxygen than would be expected.   *1 mark*

(ii)   Add hydrochloric acid to the residue.   *1 mark*

    Bubbles of colourless gas are formed.   *1 mark*

Examiner's tip

Hydrochloric acid reacts with excess magnesium to form hydrogen gas. No gas is formed when magnesium oxide reacts with hydrochloric acid.

e   Magnesium nitride   *1 mark*

Examiner's tip

Magnesium nitrate is a compound of magnesium, nitrogen **and** oxygen.

TOTAL 8 MARKS

TEST TOTAL 96 MARKS

Test B Answers

1a   The left-hand side of the magnet should be labelled S, and the right-hand side N.   *1 mark*

Examiner's tip

The direction of a magnetic field is the direction of the force on the N-seeking pole of another magnet, so it points away from the N-seeking pole and towards the S-seeking pole.

b (i)   The left-hand side of the magnet should be labelled N, and the right-hand side S.   *1 mark*
(ii)   The arrow should point from left to right.   *1 mark*

TOTAL 3 MARKS

2a   **S, P, R, Q**   *3 marks*
All correct – 3 marks, three correct – 2 marks, two or one correct – 1 mark
b (i)   **B**   *1 mark*
(ii)   **C**   *1 mark*
(iii)   **D**   *1 mark*

Examiner's tip

Fractional distillation is used to separate a mixture of liquids with different boiling points, e.g. hexane and heptane.

TOTAL 6 MARKS

3a   leaves ⟶ aphids ⟶ ladybirds ⟶ great tits ⟶ sparrowhawks   *2 marks*

Examiner's tip

Award one mark if you had two of the organisms in the wrong place

b   The leaves   *1 mark*

Examiner's tip

The producer in a food chain is always a green plant. Green plants use energy from the Sun to make food from water and carbon dioxide. Everything else in the food chain relies on this food as its source of energy.

c (i)   The great tit is a predator as it feeds on ladybirds.   *1 mark*
(ii)   The great tit is prey for the sparrowhawk.   *1 mark*
d   There is more food for the ladybirds.   *1 mark*
      So the population of ladybirds rises.   *1 mark*
e   Either mouse **or** caterpillar **or** aphids   *1 mark*

Examiner's tip

A herbivore is an animal that only eats plants.

f   The grass snakes have other food that they eat.   *1 mark*

TOTAL 9 MARKS

4a   **Y Z X W**   *3 marks*
Award 1 mark if **Y** is before **Z**, 1 mark if **Z** is before **X** and 1 mark if **X** is before **W**.
So **Y, W, X, Z** is worth 1 mark for **Y** before **Z**.

b (i)   Hydrogen   *1 mark*
(ii)   Put a lighted splint into the gas.   *1 mark*
Gas burns with a squeaky pop.   *1 mark*

Examiner's tip

Common errors are for a student to write glowing splint (used for oxygen) or a splint (not suggesting it is lit) instead of lighted splint or to forget to write the result.

TOTAL 6 MARKS

5a   Either iron filings or a compass.   *1 mark*

Examiner's tip

Iron filings show the pattern of a magnetic field. A compass shows the direction of the magnetic field at any point in the field.

b   iron   *1 mark*
c   The iron core is magnetised by the current in the coil; it has a strong magnetic field.   *1 mark*

Examiner's tip

Iron is easily magnetised and loses its magnetism easily.

TOTAL 3 MARKS

6   The correct links are:
A – processes nitrogen waste (urea)
B – exchanges gases between air and blood
C – pumps blood around the body
D – expands and contracts the lungs
E – digests food   *One mark for each one correct: 5 marks*

Examiner's tip

Questions about the jobs of different organs in the body are common in KS3 tests. Make sure that you revise them thoroughly.

TOTAL 5 MARKS

7a	An ammeter	*1 mark*
	The symbol should be drawn as an A in a circle, either side of the lamp.	*1 mark*
b	Circuit **B**	*1 mark*
c	This circuit has the greatest current.	*1 mark*
	There is a higher voltage for each lamp than in the other circuits.	*1 mark*

Examiner's tip

In a series circuit, the battery voltage is shared between the components. The greater the voltage, the greater the current.

TOTAL 5 MARKS

8a	It is an exothermic reaction.	*1 mark*
b	Iron sulphide or iron(II) sulphide.	*1 mark*
c (i)	**D**	*1 mark*
(ii)	**B**	*1 mark*
(iii)	**A**	*1 mark*

Examiner's tip

Understanding how atoms of different elements combine together in fixed numbers to form a compound is an important idea that student's fail to understand at KS3.

TOTAL 5 MARKS

9a	upward; water; boat	*One mark each: 3 marks*
b	The arrow should point vertically downwards.	*1 mark*

Examiner's tip

This force is the downward pull of the Earth. When the boat is floating the vertical forces are balanced, this means that the downward pull of the Earth is equal in size to the upward push of the water.

c	It becomes bigger.	*1 mark*
d	It becomes bigger.	*1 mark*

Examiner's tip

When the downward force increases, the boat sinks further into the water. This causes the upward force to increase.

TOTAL 6 MARKS

10a	Ball and socket	*1 mark*
b	It allows all-round movement of the arm.	*1 mark*

c	The biceps contract.	*1 mark*
	The triceps relax.	*1 mark*

TOTAL 4 MARKS

11a	Carbohydrate or fat	*1 mark*
b	Protein	*1 mark*
c (i)	cheese	*1 mark*
(ii)	cheese	*1 mark*
(iii)	For strong bones and teeth.	*1 mark*

TOTAL 5 MARKS

12a	The arrangement of particles in liquid water is irregular;	*1 mark*
	the particles are close together.	*1 mark*
	The movement is random	*1 mark*
	and relatively slow.	*1 mark*

b (i)	Particles are escaping from the liquid into the air above.	*1 mark*
	It is the high energy particles that are escaping.	*1 mark*

(ii)	The particles escaping from the liquid are blown away and cannot return to the liquid.	*1 mark*
(iii)	The layer of oil reduces evaporation by stopping the particles from escaping from the liquid.	*1 mark*

TOTAL 8 MARKS

13a (i) Water   *1 mark*
   (ii) The root   *1 mark*

Examiner's tip

Water and other minerals from the soil are absorbed by the root hairs.

b (i) Oxygen   *1 mark*
   (ii) It diffuses into the air   *1 mark*
      through the stomata in the leaves.   *1 mark*

Examiner's tip

Gas exchange between a plant and the air takes place through the stomata. These are found mainly on the underneath of leaves. They are opened and closed by guard cells.

   (iii) Light **or** sunlight **or** the Sun.   *1 mark*
   c The green parts.   *1 mark*

Examiner's tip

The green colour in plants is due to the substance chlorophyll. This absorbs the energy needed for photosynthesis.

d (i) The light level changes.   *1 mark*
   (ii) The grower could increase the concentration of carbon dioxide.   *1 mark*

TOTAL 9 MARKS

14a

	Copper nitrate	Magnesium nitrate	Silver nitrate	Zinc nitrate
Copper	✗	✗	✓	✗
Magnesium	✓	✗	✓	✓
Silver	✗	✗	✗	✗
Zinc	✓	✗	✓	✗

Award one mark for each correct row: 3 marks

b Colourless solution turns blue   *1 mark*
   Silvery coating forms on copper   *1 mark*
c copper + silver nitrate $\longrightarrow$ copper nitrate + silver   *2 marks*

Examiner's tip

You should be able to summarise chemical reactions by writing word equations.

TOTAL 7 MARKS

15a   The wind   *1 mark*

b   The driving force is greater than the resistive force.   *1 mark*

> ### Examiner's tip
> Whether an object speeds up, slows down or maintains a steady speed depends on the balance of the forces acting. If the forces acting on an object are balanced, it stays at rest or maintains a steady speed. Unbalanced forces cause a change in speed or direction or both.

c   It slows down.   *1 mark*
Because there is no longer a driving force.   *1 mark*

TOTAL 4 MARKS

16a   **D**   *1 mark*

b   A book scatters light or reflects it in all directions.   *1 mark*

c   **E**   *1 mark*

> ### Examiner's tip
> The image in a mirror is always the same distance directly behind the mirror as the object is in front of the mirror.

d   They are both upright.   *1 mark*
They are the same size.   *1 mark*

TOTAL 5 MARKS

17a   It vibrates or oscillates.   *1 mark*

> ### Examiner's tip
> All sounds are caused by the vibration of an object; in musical instruments it is usually either a string or an air column that vibrates.

b   The cone moves further.   *1 mark*

> ### Examiner's tip
> The amplitude of a vibration is the greatest displacement from the rest position.

c   It sounds louder.   *1 mark*

TOTAL 3 MARKS

18a   The arrow should point towards the centre of the Earth.   *1 mark*

Examiner's tip

The force that keeps the satellite in orbit is a gravitational force. It is the Earth's pull on the satellite.

b   *Any two from:*
navigation
monitoring the weather
surveillance
communications
astronomy   *One mark each: 2 marks*

TOTAL 3 MARKS

TEST TOTAL 96 MARKS

1a   **A** – placenta; **B** – amniotic sac; **C** – amniotic fluid   *3 marks*

b   The umbilical cord takes oxygen and nutrients to the fetus   *1 mark*

       and also transfers waste products from the fetus to the mother.   *1 mark*

Examiner's tip

Pupils frequently score the first mark but do not score the second. The indication of two marks for the question should help you to add the second statement.

TOTAL 5 MARKS

2a   **A** and **B** act as a control.   *1 mark*

Examiner's tip

The colour of the solution in tubes **A** and **B** should remain unchanged throughout. If they do not, something is wrong and other results could not be relied upon.

b   Tube **C** – the change from red to yellow indicates more carbon dioxide present.   *1 mark*

       Respiration produces carbon dioxide.   *1 mark*

       Tube **D** – the change from red to purple indicates less carbon dioxide present.   *1 mark*

       Photosynthesis uses up carbon dioxide.   *1 mark*

Examiner's tip

Pupils frequently forget that respiration takes place in a plant in sunlight and out of sunlight. However, in sunlight the respiration is swamped by the photosynthesis taking place.

TOTAL 5 MARKS

3a   Four points correctly plotted   *2 marks*

       Deduct one mark for each error.

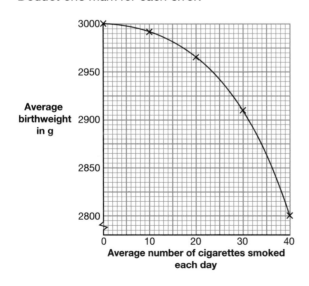

b	Correctly drawn curve	*1 mark*
c	31 cigarettes	*1 mark*

Examiner's tip

The best line is a curve and not a straight line. The examiner reads the answer from the graph you have drawn.

d	Alcohol and drugs	*2 marks*

TOTAL 6 MARKS

4a Calcium carbonate + hydrochloric acid $\longrightarrow$ calcium carbonate + water
+ carbon dioxide   *1 mark*

$CaCO_3 + 2HCl \longrightarrow CaCl_2 + H_2O + CO_2$ *2 marks*

Examiner's tip

At Level 8 you will have to be able to write balanced symbol equations.

b	Test with limewater	*1 mark*
	Turns limewater milky	*1 mark*
c	Carbon dioxide reacts with water to form carbonic acid	*1 mark*
	Carbonic acid reacts with marble chip	*1 mark*
	Forms calcium hydrogencarbonate	*1 mark*

Examiner's tip

No marks would be given for answering calcium carbonate reacts with water.

In the past KS3 tests have not asked questions requiring longer answers. These are required by all GCSE Boards for GCSE. Questions requiring longer answers will probably be set in KS3 in the future.

The balanced equation below would score all three marks in part **c**.

$CaCO_3 + H_2O + CO_2 \longrightarrow Ca(HCO_3)_2$

TOTAL 8 MARKS

5a (i)	At night water freezes	*1 mark*
	and expands	*1 mark*
	causing large forces which break up the rock.	*1 mark*
(ii)	Weathering	*1 mark*
b	Expansion when rocks are heated and contraction when cooled	*1 mark*
	causes stresses which break up rocks.	*1 mark*
	Wind blows sand.	*1 mark*
	Moving sand wears away rock.	*1 mark*

Examiner's tip

This question is designed to emphasise the differences between weathering and erosion. Erosion is the wearing away of rocks by moving water, ice, sand, etc.

TOTAL 8 MARKS

6a Here are the completed diagrams.

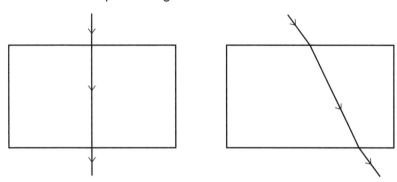

Award one mark for showing the light continuing in the same direction in the left-hand diagram.   *1 mark*

Award one mark for each correct change of direction shown in the right-hand diagram.   *2 marks*

Examiner's tip

The change in direction when light crosses a boundary is often described with reference to the normal line. This is a line drawn at right angles to the boundary. Light that travels along the normal line does not change direction.

For light that meets the boundary in any other direction, the change of direction is towards the normal line as it passes into glass or plastic and away from the normal line as it passes back into air.

b   Refraction   *1 mark*

c (i)   It separates into colours.   *1 mark*

(ii)   It shows that white light is a mixture of different colours.   *1 mark*

Examiner's tip

Rainbows are caused by the dispersion of white light passing through water droplets.

TOTAL 6 MARKS

7a   The Moon is seen by the light that it reflects   *1 mark*
        from the Sun.   *1 mark*

Examiner's tip

Stars are so hot they give out their own light. Planets and moons are much cooler, they can only be seen by light that is reflected off them.

b (i)   The pole star   *1 mark*

(ii)   The Earth's rotation on its axis makes the other stars appear to move.   *1 mark*

Examiner's tip

The pole star appears not to move because it is straight above the axis of rotation.

(iii)   21 hours   *1 mark*

Examiner's tip

If you answered '20 hours 59 minutes' then you clearly have a very good understanding of why the stars appear to rotate. They seem to go round once each day because of the Earth's rotation on its axis, and an additional once each year because of the Earth's movement around the Sun.

TOTAL 5 MARKS

8a   1500 m   *1 mark*

  b   120 s   *1 mark*

Examiner's tip

These two questions are testing how well you can read information from a graph.

c   distance travelled = 2500 m in 250 s   *1 mark*
         speed = distance travelled ÷ time taken   *1 mark*
                = 2500 m ÷ 250 s = 10 m/s   *1 mark*

TOTAL 5 MARKS

TEST TOTAL 48 MARKS

Determining your level

FINDING YOUR LEVEL IN TESTS A AND B

When you have completed and marked a test, enter the total number of marks you scored for each question on the Marking grid overleaf. Then add them up. Using the total for each test, look at the charts below to determine your level for each test.

Test A

Level 3 or below	Level 4	Level 5	Level 6	Level 7 or above
up to 12	13–33	34–51	52–71	72+

Test B

Level 3 or below	Level 4	Level 5	Level 6	Level 7 or above
up to 12	13–33	34–51	52–71	72+

FINDING YOUR OVERALL LEVEL IN SCIENCE

After you have worked out separate levels for Tests A and B, add up your total marks for the two tests. Use this total and the chart below to determine your overall level in Science. The chart also shows you how your level in these tests compares with the target level for your age group.

Total for Tests A and B

Level 3 or below	Level 4	Level 5	Level 6	Level 7 or above
up to 24	25–66	67–102	103–142	143+
Working towards target level for age group		Working at target level for age group		Working beyond target level

FINDING YOUR LEVEL IN THE EXTENSION PAPER

If you have tried the Extension paper you can work out your level using the marking grid below.

Extension paper

Below Level 6	Level 6	Level 7
up to 27	28–37	38–48

FINDING OUT WHETHER YOU ARE STRONGER IN ONE AT

In the tables on page 66 the questions are divided into AT2 (Biology), AT3 (Chemistry) and AT4 (Physics). There are 64 marks for each AT in Test A and Test B and 16 marks for each AT in the Extension paper.

Add up your score for each AT. These totals may help you to decide where to concentrate in your revision.

Marking grid

Question	AT	Marks available	Marks scored	Question	AT	Marks available	Marks scored
1	4	5		8	2	11	
2	2	14		9	4	4	
3	4	6		10	3	9	
4	3	7		11	4	6	
5	2	7		12	4	3	
6	3	8		13	4	4	
7	4	4		14	3	8	
				Total		96	

Question	AT	Marks available	Marks scored	Question	AT	Marks available	Marks scored
1	4	3		10	2	4	
2	3	6		11	2	5	
3	2	9		12	3	8	
4	3	6		13	2	9	
5	4	3		14	3	7	
6	2	5		15	4	4	
7	4	5		16	4	5	
8	3	5		17	4	3	
9	4	6		18	4	3	
				Total		96	

Question	AT	Marks available	Marks scored	Question	AT	Marks available	Marks scored
1	2	5		5	3	8	
2	2	5		6	4	6	
3	2	6		7	4	5	
4	3	8		8	4	5	
				Total		48	